the CRAZY world of LOVE

Cartoons by Roland Fiddy

EXLEY

MT. KISCO, NEW YORK · WATFORD, UK

"Oh, John, I've never met anyone like you before …
Oh, Mark, I've never met anyone like you before …
Oh, Steve, I've never met anyone like you before …"

"Susan was right – you _ARE_ homely!"

"Not _THOSE_ thoughts!"

"I don't know her name ... Just write 'the beautiful girl at the bacon counter in our supermarket'."

"I think I should warn you Dad's a bit Victorian!"

"I'm not a good judge of men, so I always let Bruce decide who comes in for coffee!"

1.

2.

3.

4.

5.

"And you still have the wavy hair I fell for, George!"

"My, you really are scared of women, aren't you?"

"I hope that young tearaway hasn't been hanging around!"

"We'll have to stop meeting like this – I forget what you look like!"

Irresistible

1.

2.

"Excuse me, Sir, but if you don't replace your tie I must ask you to leave!"

"You might as well face it – he's stood you up!"

"These are my parents – they are inseparable!"

"You're just testing me, aren't you Dorothy?"

"There's someone else, isn't there?"

"*I'm not a bit tired, dear. It's only us old folks who have time to listen to your problems!*"

"That's what I love about you, Lorna – you're such
a good listener!"

"Our love has grown with the years!"

"When Mary left me I went to pieces – if I hadn't
met you, Gloria, I think I'd have gone out of my mind!"

"Either we are witnesses to a unique astronomical phenomenon, Miss Johnson, or I'm in love!"

BOY MEETS GIRL!

4. & 4a.

5. & 5a.

6. & 6a.

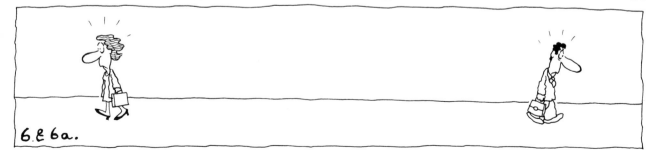

"Are you <u>sure</u> she's expecting you?"

"Perhaps you would prefer to order later, Sir?"

1.

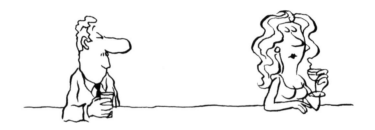

2.

3.

4.

5.

6.

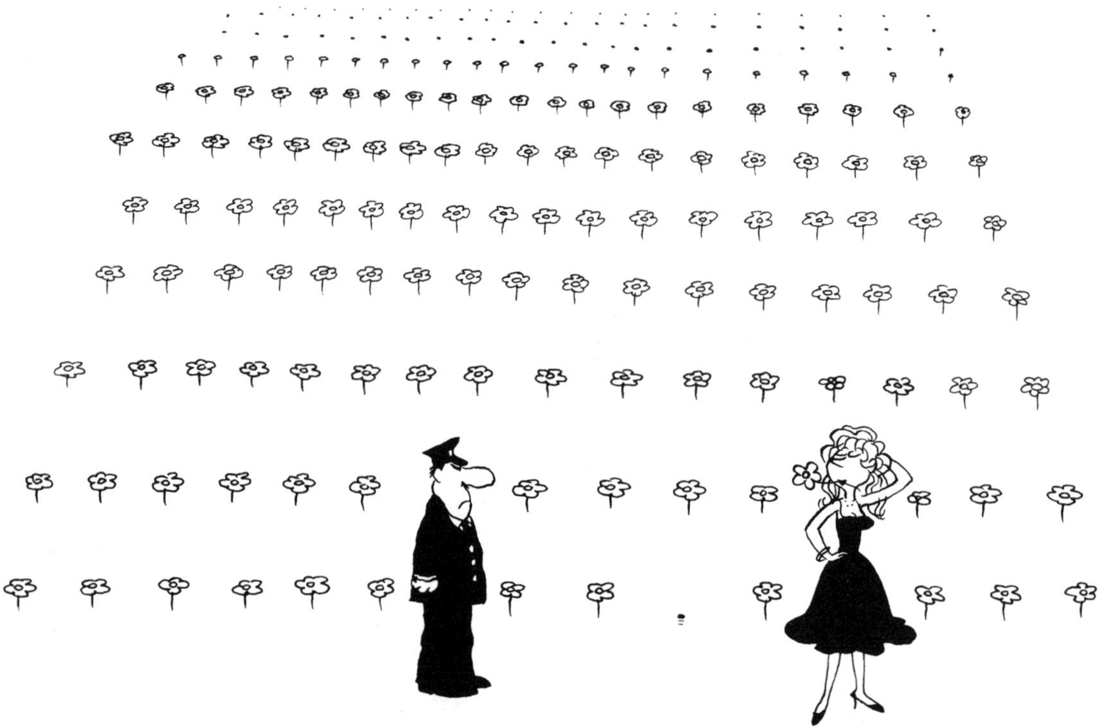

"When I was a boy, we had to entertain ourselves!"

"All these years we've been together Charlie, you've never changed!"

*"I told the tattooist to put 'mother' – unfortunately
he was hard of hearing ..."*

1.

2.

6.

7.

8.

"But first, I have a suggestion …"

"Don't let a newspaper smother our great love!"

"Him? Just an old hanger-on!"

"John! No, I'm not doing anything – just sitting around."

"Alone at last!!"

"Dad's really taken to you!"

1.

2.

3.

"She won't be long – she's just shaving her legs."

"I take it you're going out with Linda this evening, son?"

"*I think it makes you look distinguished!*"

"I need more time, Henry!"

"The telephone is red hot again!"

*"That's what I love about you Emily – you always
laugh at my joke!"*

"*On second thoughts, you look better with them on.*"

"I have a confession – under the feathers I'm bald!"

"Don't tell me – she's in love <u>again</u>!"

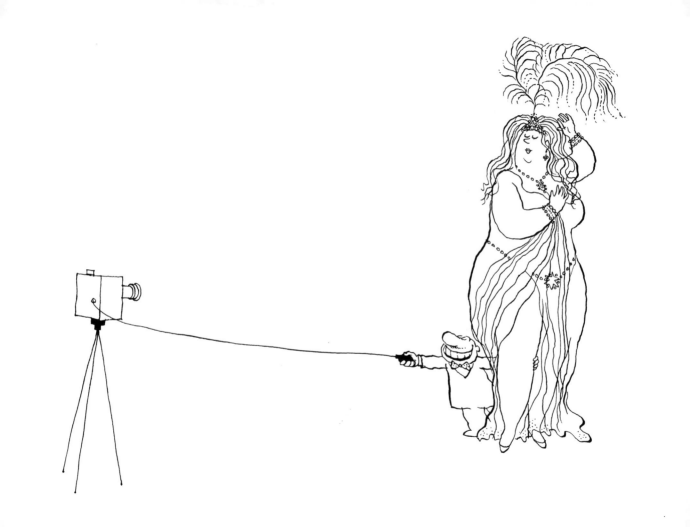

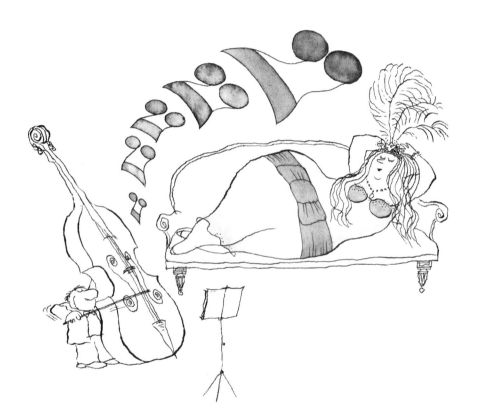

"*Macho men do not appeal to me, Bernard!*"

"We are in love with you, John Brown!"

"Sometimes I wish you would express your abiding love some other way!"

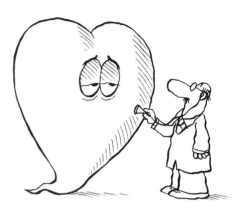

1.

OVER ▶

2.

3.

"Why don't you marry him and put us both out of our misery?"

Books in the "Crazy World" series
($4.99 £2.99 paperback)

The Crazy World of Cats (Bill Stott)
The Crazy World of Cricket (Bill Stott)
The Crazy World of Gardening (Bill Stott)
The Crazy World of Golf (Mike Scott)
The Crazy World of the Greens (Barry Knowles)
The Crazy World of the Handyman (Roland Fiddy)
The Crazy World of Hospitals (Bill Stott)
The Crazy World of Housework (Bill Stott)
The Crazy World of Marriage (Bill Stott)
The Crazy World of Rugby (Bill Stott)
The Crazy World of Sailing (Peter Rigby)
The Crazy World of Sex (David Pye)

The Mini Joke Book series
($6.99 £3.99 hardback)

These attractive 64 page mini joke books are illustrated
in colour throughout by Bill Stott.

A Binge of Diet Jokes
A Bouquet of Wedding Jokes
A Feast of After Dinner Jokes
A Portfolio of Business Jokes
A Round of Golf Jokes
A Romp of Naughty Jokes
A Spread of Over-40s Jokes

The "Fanatics" series ($4.99 £2.99 paperback)

The **Fanatic's Guides** are perfect presents for everyone
with a hobby that has got out of hand. Eighty pages of
hilarious black and white cartoons by Roland Fiddy

The Fanatic's Guide to the Bed
The Fanatic's Guide to Cats
The Fanatic's Guide to Computers
The Fanatic's Guide to Dads
The Fanatic's Guide to Diets
The Fanatic's Guide to Dogs
The Fanatic's Guide to Husbands
The Fanatic's Guide to Money
The Fanatic's Guide to Sex
The Fanatic's Guide to Skiing

Great Britain: Order these super books from your local
bookseller or from Exley Publications Ltd, 16 Chalk
Hill, Watford, Herts WD1 4BN. (Please send £1.25 to
cover postage and packing on 1 book, £2.50 on 2 or
more books.)

Other books in the series:
The Crazy World of Cats (Bill Stott)
The Crazy World of Cricket (Bill Stott)
The Crazy World of Gardening (Bill Stott)
The Crazy World of Golf (Mike Scott)
The Crazy World of the Greens (Barry Knowles)
The Crazy World of The Handyman (Roland Fiddy)
The Crazy World of Hospitals (Bill Stott)
The Crazy World of Housework (Bill Stott)
The Crazy World of Marriage (Bill Stott)
The Crazy World of Rugby (Bill Stott)
The Crazy World of Sailing (Peter Rigby)
The Crazy World of Sex (David Pye)

This paperback edition published simultaneously in 1992 by Exley
Publications Ltd. in Great Britain, and Exley Giftbooks in the USA.
First hardback edition published in Great Britain in 1988 by Exley
Publications Ltd.

Copyright © Roland Fiddy, 1988

ISBN 1-85015-387-6

Printed in Spain by Grafo S.A., Bilbao.

Exley Publications Ltd, 16 Chalk Hill, Watford, Herts WD1 4BN,
United Kingdom.
Exley Giftbooks, 359 East Main Street, Suite 3D, Mount Kisco,
NY 10549, USA.